WALT DISNEY'S

A Visit to Disneyland

Authorized Edition

by Mabel Watts

illustrated by
Stan Tusan

Photographs by Roger Davidson
and the Walt Disney Studios

WHITMAN PUBLISHING COMPANY

RACINE, WISCONSIN

Printed in the U.S.A. by Western Printing and Lithographing Company

Come to the Magic Kingdom,
Join the adventurous band,
Walk through the turnstile,
Into the square,
And LOOK—

You're in Disneyland!

Riding top-deck in an omnibus,
You're back in Great-Grandmother's day.
You turn back the clock
As you chug down the block
Along Main Street, U.S.A.

MAIN ST.

There are horse-drawn trolleys and carriages
And funny old cars by the score.
You see a parade,
A penny arcade,
And many an old-fashioned store.

Prance and dance to the music,
Keep in step with its cheerful beat,
For the Disneyland band
Is the best in the land
To tickle the soles of your feet.

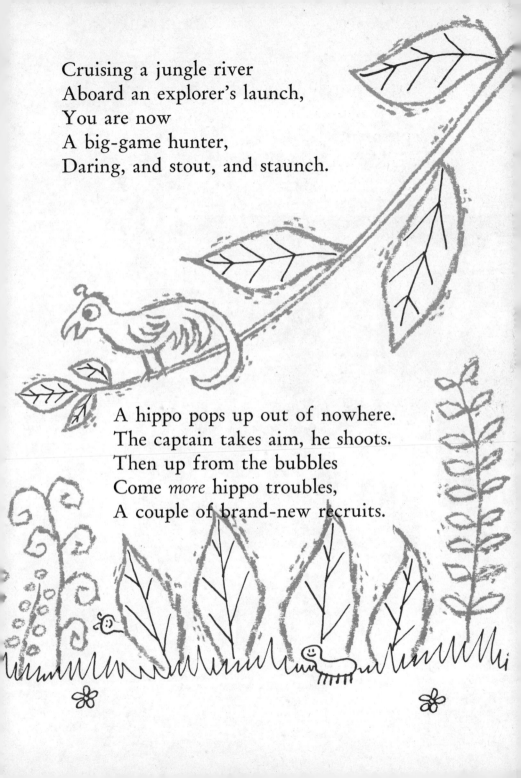

Cruising a jungle river
Aboard an explorer's launch,
You are now
A big-game hunter,
Daring, and stout, and staunch.

A hippo pops up out of nowhere.
The captain takes aim, he shoots.
Then up from the bubbles
Come *more* hippo troubles,
A couple of brand-new recruits.

There are orchids galore on the tropical shore,
And savages eager to seize you.
Elephants keep cool
In their own private pool,
And gorillas look ready to squeeze you.

Climb up the stairs to the Tree House
Of Swiss Family Robinson fame.
Be a castaway
In this hideaway,
Shipwrecked, but happy and game.

A sight-seeing trip on this steamer
Is exciting and certain to please.
Give the whistle a jerk,
Watch the paddle wheel work,
And try out the fine plush settees.

A fort and a cave await the young and the brave
On Tom Sawyer Island shore.
And the Huck Finn Raft,
A sturdy log craft,
Will ferry you there to explore.

How do you paddle a war canoe
When you happen to be one of the paleface crew?
Hold tight to your oar,
Push off from shore,
And row like the Indians do.

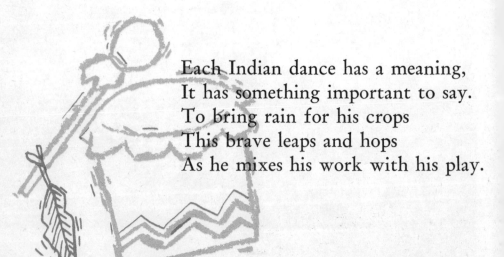

Each Indian dance has a meaning,
It has something important to say.
To bring rain for his crops
This brave leaps and hops
As he mixes his work with his play.

Crane your neck from the keelboat's deck,
To scan the wild frontier.
In your coonskin cap
With your grub and your map
You're a fearless, brave pioneer.

You are ready to tour Nature's Wonderland
Where the deer and the bighorn feed.
You'll see smart, fishing bears,
Beavers building in pairs,
As you ride on your surefooted steed.

If you have a question for Alice,
The Mad Hatter, or the merry March Hare,
Don't be timid or shy,
Ask, "How?" "What?" or "Why?"
For a chance such as this is quite rare.

Enter this storybook castle
With its drawbridge, its towers, its steeple.
No need to speak low,
Or to walk tippy-toe,
Sleeping Beauty's awake, greeting people.

The dwarfs are kindly and friendly.
There is something delightful about them.
Snow White loves every one,
And when all's said and done,
She'd not venture forth without them.

Pick a good steed full of spirit and speed,
Handsome, high-stepping, and proud.
On *this* carrousel
Every horse must excel,
For only the best are allowed.

This canalboat takes you through
   Storybook Land,
While the scenery reels off the pages.
You pass spots old and sweet,
Places small, quaint, and neat,
From the tales you have known for ages.

Be a lion with a mane, on the Casey Jr. train,
Be a dancing circus bear going places.
Be a leopard in a cage,
Or a tiger in a rage,
Or a monkey making funny monkey faces.

Ride high on Tomorrowland's Monorail train.
Take a rocket trip clear to the moon.
You can cross outer space
At such a wild pace
That you'll be there and back very soon.

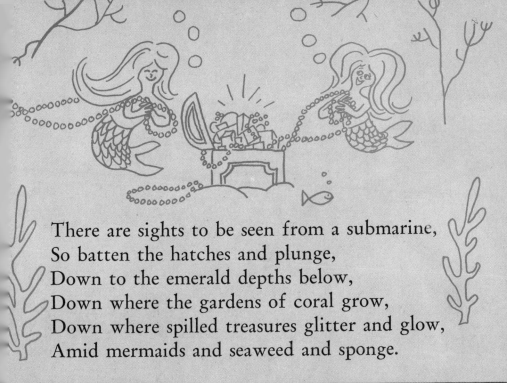

There are sights to be seen from a submarine,
So batten the hatches and plunge,
Down to the emerald depths below,
Down where the gardens of coral grow,
Down where spilled treasures glitter and glow,
Amid mermaids and seaweed and sponge.

The pilot who flies in an Astrojet
Can be *you*, at the helm, commanding.
Swift, dashing, and airy,
(Though a tiny bit scary!)
It's a great flight from takeoff to landing.

Follow the leader, obey all the rules,
You're driving Autopia style.
This highway is play,
All the traffic's one way,
And the rule of the road is *smile*.

Leave adventure and magic behind you.
But please don't shed one single tear.
The way Disneyland's growing
There's no way of knowing
What surprise you'll find *next* time you're here!